The Tottering
2024 Diary

Contact Numbers

Name

Tel

Name

Tel

Name

Tel

Name

Tel

Name

Tel

This Diary Belongs To...

Name

Address

Postcode

Telephone

Work

Mobile

Fax

E-mail

2024

	JANUARY				
Monday	1	8	15	22	29
Tuesday	2	9	16	23	30
Wednesday	3	10	17	24	31
Thursday	4	11	18	25	
Friday	5	12	19	26	
Saturday	**6**	**13**	**20**	**27**	
Sunday	**7**	**14**	**21**	**28**	

	FEBRUARY				
Monday		5	12	19	26
Tuesday		6	13	20	27
Wednesday		7	14	21	28
Thursday	1	8	15	22	29
Friday	2	9	16	23	
Saturday	**3**	**10**	**17**	**24**	
Sunday	**4**	**11**	**18**	**25**	

	MARCH				
Monday		4	11	18	25
Tuesday		5	12	19	26
Wednesday		6	13	20	27
Thursday		7	14	21	28
Friday	1	8	15	22	29
Saturday	**2**	**9**	**16**	**23**	**30**
Sunday	**3**	**10**	**17**	**24**	**31**

	APRIL				
Monday	1	8	15	22	29
Tuesday	2	9	16	23	30
Wednesday	3	10	17	24	
Thursday	4	11	18	25	
Friday	5	12	19	26	
Saturday	**6**	**13**	**20**	**27**	
Sunday	**7**	**14**	**21**	**28**	

	MAY				
Monday		6	13	20	27
Tuesday		7	14	21	28
Wednesday	1	8	15	22	29
Thursday	2	9	16	23	30
Friday	3	10	17	24	31
Saturday	**4**	**11**	**18**	**25**	
Sunday	**5**	**12**	**19**	**26**	

	JUNE				
Monday		3	10	17	24
Tuesday		4	11	18	25
Wednesday		5	12	19	26
Thursday		6	13	20	27
Friday		7	14	21	28
Saturday	**1**	**8**	**15**	**22**	**29**
Sunday	**2**	**9**	**16**	**23**	**30**

	JULY				
Monday	1	8	15	22	29
Tuesday	2	9	16	23	30
Wednesday	3	10	17	24	31
Thursday	4	11	18	25	
Friday	5	12	19	26	
Saturday	**6**	**13**	**20**	**27**	
Sunday	**7**	**14**	**21**	**28**	

	AUGUST				
Monday		5	12	19	26
Tuesday		6	13	20	27
Wednesday		7	14	21	28
Thursday	1	8	15	22	29
Friday	2	9	16	23	30
Saturday	**3**	**10**	**17**	**24**	**31**
Sunday	**4**	**11**	**18**	**25**	

	SEPTEMBER				
Monday	30	2	9	16	23
Tuesday		3	10	17	24
Wednesday		4	11	18	25
Thursday		5	12	19	26
Friday		6	13	20	27
Saturday		**7**	**14**	**21**	**28**
Sunday	**1**	**8**	**15**	**22**	**29**

	OCTOBER				
Monday		7	14	21	28
Tuesday	1	8	15	22	29
Wednesday	2	9	16	23	30
Thursday	3	10	17	24	31
Friday	4	11	18	25	
Saturday	**5**	**12**	**19**	**26**	
Sunday	**6**	**13**	**20**	**27**	

	NOVEMBER				
Monday		4	11	18	25
Tuesday		5	12	19	26
Wednesday		6	13	20	27
Thursday		7	14	21	28
Friday	1	8	15	22	29
Saturday	**2**	**9**	**16**	**23**	**30**
Sunday	**3**	**10**	**17**	**24**	

	DECEMBER				
Monday	30	2	9	16	23
Tuesday	31	3	10	17	24
Wednesday		4	11	18	25
Thursday		5	12	19	26
Friday		6	13	20	27
Saturday		**7**	**14**	**21**	**28**
Sunday	**1**	**8**	**15**	**22**	**29**

2025

JANUARY

Monday		6	13	20	27
Tuesday		7	14	21	28
Wednesday	1	8	15	22	29
Thursday	2	9	16	23	30
Friday	3	10	17	24	31
Saturday	**4**	**11**	**18**	**25**	
Sunday	**5**	**12**	**19**	**26**	

FEBRUARY

Monday		3	10	17	24
Tuesday		4	11	18	25
Wednesday		5	12	19	26
Thursday		6	13	20	27
Friday		7	14	21	28
Saturday	**1**	**8**	**15**	**22**	
Sunday	**2**	**9**	**16**	**23**	

MARCH

Monday	31	3	10	17	24
Tuesday		4	11	18	25
Wednesday		5	12	19	26
Thursday		6	13	20	27
Friday		7	14	21	28
Saturday	**1**	**8**	**15**	**22**	**29**
Sunday	**2**	**9**	**16**	**23**	**30**

APRIL

Monday		7	14	21	28
Tuesday	1	8	15	22	29
Wednesday	2	9	16	23	30
Thursday	3	10	17	24	
Friday	4	11	18	25	
Saturday	**5**	**12**	**19**	**26**	
Sunday	**6**	**13**	**20**	**27**	

MAY

Monday		5	12	19	26
Tuesday		6	13	20	27
Wednesday		7	14	21	28
Thursday	1	8	15	22	29
Friday	2	9	16	23	30
Saturday	**3**	**10**	**17**	**24**	**31**
Sunday	**4**	**11**	**18**	**25**	

JUNE

Monday	30	2	9	16	23
Tuesday		3	10	17	24
Wednesday		4	11	18	25
Thursday		5	12	19	26
Friday		6	13	20	27
Saturday		**7**	**14**	**21**	**28**
Sunday	**1**	**8**	**15**	**22**	**29**

JULY

Monday		7	14	21	28
Tuesday	1	8	15	22	29
Wednesday	2	9	16	23	30
Thursday	3	10	17	24	31
Friday	4	11	18	25	
Saturday	**5**	**12**	**19**	**26**	
Sunday	**6**	**13**	**20**	**27**	

AUGUST

Monday		4	11	18	25
Tuesday		5	12	19	26
Wednesday		6	13	20	27
Thursday		7	14	21	28
Friday	1	8	15	22	29
Saturday	**2**	**9**	**16**	**23**	**30**
Sunday	**3**	**10**	**17**	**24**	**31**

SEPTEMBER

Monday	1	8	15	22	29
Tuesday	2	9	16	23	30
Wednesday	3	10	17	24	
Thursday	4	11	18	25	
Friday	5	12	19	26	
Saturday	**6**	**13**	**20**	**27**	
Sunday	**7**	**14**	**21**	**28**	

OCTOBER

Monday		6	13	20	27
Tuesday		7	14	21	28
Wednesday	1	8	15	22	29
Thursday	2	9	16	23	30
Friday	3	10	17	24	31
Saturday	**4**	**11**	**18**	**25**	
Sunday	**5**	**12**	**19**	**26**	

NOVEMBER

Monday		3	10	17	24
Tuesday		4	11	18	25
Wednesday		5	12	19	26
Thursday		6	13	20	27
Friday		7	14	21	28
Saturday	**1**	**8**	**15**	**22**	**29**
Sunday	**2**	**9**	**16**	**23**	**30**

DECEMBER

Monday	1	8	15	22	29
Tuesday	2	9	16	23	30
Wednesday	3	10	17	24	31
Thursday	4	11	18	25	
Friday	5	12	19	26	
Saturday	**6**	**13**	**20**	**27**	
Sunday	**7**	**14**	**21**	**28**	

Conversions

1 in = 2.54 cm	1 in² = 6.4516 cm²
1 cm = 0.3937 in	1 cm² = 0.155 in²
1 ft = 0.3048 m	1 ft² = 0.0929 m²
1 m = 3.2808 ft	1 m² = 10.7639 ft²
1 yd = 0.9144 m	1 mile² = 2.59 km²
1 m = 1.0936 yd	1 km² = 0.3861 miles²
1 mile = 1.6093 km	1 acre = 0.4047 ha
1 km = 0.6214 miles	1 ha = 2.471 acres
1 in³ = 16.387 cm³	1 UK gal = 4.546 l
1 cm³ = 0.06102 in³	1 l = 0.22 UK gal
1 ft³ = 0.02832 m³	1 oz = 28.3495 g
1 m³ = 35.3147 ft³	1 g = 0.03527 oz
1 yd³ = 0.76456 m³	1 lb = 453.59 g
1 m³ = 1.30795 yd³	1 g = 0.002205 lb
1 US gal = 3.7854 l	1 kg = 2.2046 lb
1 l = 0.2642 US gal	1 t (long) = 1016.0469 kg
1 US gal = 0.8327 UK gal	1 kg = 0.00098 t (long)

Useful Contacts

Tourist Information: www.visitbritain.com
Telephone: 020 7578 1000

Healthcare: www.nhs.uk
Telephone: 111 (non-emergency calls)
Telephone: 999 (emergency calls)

Police: www.police.uk
Telephone: 101 (non-emergency calls)
Telephone: 999 (emergency calls)

Government Services: www.gov.uk

Doctor:

Dentist:

Hospital:

Local Police Station:

Local Council:

Medical Information:

Car Insurance:

Car Breakdown:

Sometimes it amazes me
how well men actually can multitask
when they want to ...

Oh! I know ! My husband's incredible at it
- he can listen, ignore and forget
simultaneously...

Notes

_____

_____

_____

_____

_____

_____

_____

_____

_____

_____

_____

_____

_____

_____

_____

_____

_____

January

Mon	Tue	Wed	Thu	Fri	Sat	Sun
1	2	3	4	5	6	7
8	9	10	11	12	13	14
15	16	17	18	19	20	21
22	23	24	25	26	27	28
29	30	31				

January

Monday
1

New Year's Day
(Holiday UK, R. of Ireland, USA, CAN, AUS, NZL)

Tuesday
2

Holiday (SCT, NZL)

Wednesday
3

Thursday
4 ◑

Friday
5

Saturday
6

Sunday
7

Notes

January

Monday
8

Tuesday
9

Wednesday
10

Thursday
11   ●

Friday
12

Saturday
13

Sunday
14

Notes

T W T F S S M T W T F S S M T W
16 17 18 19 20 21 22 23 24 25 26 27 28 29 30 31

January

Martin Luther King, Jr. Day
(Holiday USA)

◑

Friday
19

Saturday
20

Sunday
21

Notes

January

Monday
22

Tuesday
23

Wednesday
24

Thursday
25   ○

Burns Night (SCT)

	M	T	W	T	F	S	S	M	T	W	T	F	S	S	M
JAN	1	2	3	4	5	6	7	8	9	10	11	12	13	14	15

Friday
26

Australia Day (Holiday AUS)

Saturday
27

Sunday
28

Notes

I don't even know what 'WOKE' means ...

Our son, Honjon and his partner are 'WOKE'
I think to our generation it means
'Woefully Obvious Knowledge Expounders'

Notes

February

Mon	Tue	Wed	Thu	Fri	Sat	Sun
			1	2	3	4
5	6	7	8	9	10	11
12	13	14	15	16	17	18
19	20	21	22	23	24	25
26	27	28	29			

January/February

Monday
29

Tuesday
30

Wednesday
31

Thursday
1

◑

Friday
2

Saturday
3

Sunday
4

Notes

February

Monday
5

St Brigid's Day (Holiday R. of Ireland)

Tuesday
6

Waitangi Day (Holiday NZL)

Wednesday
7

Thursday
8

Chinese New Year - Year of the Dragon

Notes

February

Monday
12

Tuesday
13

Shrove Tuesday

Wednesday
14

St Valentine's Day
Ash Wednesday

Thursday
15

◗

Notes

T	F	S	S	M	T	W	T	F	S	S	M	T	W	T
15	16	17	18	19	20	21	22	23	24	25	26	27	28	29

February

Monday
19

Presidents' Day (Holiday USA)

Tuesday
20

Wednesday
21

Thursday
22

Friday
23

○

Saturday
24

Sunday
25

Notes

I am an optimist ...

If I take a step backwards
after taking one step forwards
It's not the end of the world...

It's a Cha-Cha ...

Notes

March

Mon	Tue	Wed	Thu	Fri	Sat	Sun
				1	2	3
4	5	6	7	8	9	10
11	12	13	14	15	16	17
18	19	20	21	22	23	24
25	26	27	28	29	30	31

February/March

Monday
26

Tuesday
27

Wednesday
28

Thursday
29

Friday
1

St David's Day

Saturday
2

◑

Sunday
3

Notes

March

Monday
4

Tuesday
5

Wednesday
6

Thursday
7

Friday
8

Saturday
9

● Sunday
10

Mothering Sunday (UK, R. of Ireland)
Ramadan Begins at Sundown

Notes

March

Monday
11

Tuesday
12

Wednesday
13

Thursday
14

Friday
15

Saturday
16

◑ Sunday
17

St Patrick's Day

Notes

S S M T W T F S S M T W T F S S
16 17 18 19 20 21 22 23 24 25 26 27 28 29 30 31

March

Monday
18

Holiday (N. Ireland, R. of Ireland)

Tuesday
19

Wednesday
20

Thursday
21

Friday
22

Saturday
23

Sunday
24

Notes

March

○

Good Friday (Holiday UK, CAN, AUS, NZL)

Easter Sunday
British Summer Time begins

Notes

' FEMTEX '

An oestrogen charged weapon that
is unstable and can explode
at a second's notice !

Notes

April

Mon	Tue	Wed	Thu	Fri	Sat	Sun
1	2	3	4	5	6	7
8	9	10	11	12	13	14
15	16	17	18	19	20	21
22	23	24	25	26	27	28
29	30					

April

Monday
1

Easter Monday (Holiday UK except SCT, R. of Ireland, CAN, AUS, NZL)

Tuesday
2 ◗

Wednesday
3

Thursday
4

Friday
5

Saturday
6

Sunday
7

Notes

April

Monday
8

●

Tuesday
9

Eid al-Fitr Begins at Sundown

Wednesday
10

Thursday
11

	M	T	W	T	F	S	S	M	T	W	T	F	S	S	M
APR	1	2	3	4	5	6	7	8	9	10	11	12	13	14	15

Friday
12

Saturday
13

Sunday
14

Notes

April

Monday
15

Tuesday
16

Wednesday
17

Thursday
18

Friday
19

Saturday
20

Sunday
21

Notes

April

Monday
22

Passover Begins at Sundown

Tuesday
23

St George's Day

Wednesday   ○
24

Thursday
25

Anzac Day (Holiday AUS, NZL)

Friday
26

Saturday
27

Sunday
28

Notes

You can't expect me to be in
perfect shape -

I've just had a grandchild ...

Notes

_____

_____

_____

_____

_____

_____

_____

_____

_____

_____

_____

_____

_____

_____

_____

_____

_____

_____

May

Mon	Tue	Wed	Thu	Fri	Sat	Sun
		1	2	3	4	5
6	7	8	9	10	11	12
13	14	15	16	17	18	19
20	21	22	23	24	25	26
27	28	29	30	31		

April/May

Monday
29

Tuesday
30

Passover Ends at Sundown

Wednesday
1   ◑

Thursday
2

Friday
3

Saturday
4

Sunday
5

Notes

May

Monday
6

Holiday (UK, R. of Ireland)

Tuesday
7

Wednesday
8 ●

Thursday
9

Friday
10

Saturday
11

Sunday
12

Mother's Day (USA, CAN, AUS, NZL)

Notes

May

Monday
13

Tuesday
14

Wednesday
15

Thursday
16

Friday
17

Saturday
18

Sunday
19

Notes

May

Monday
20

Victoria Day (Holiday CAN)

Tuesday
21

Wednesday
22

Thursday
23   ○

Friday
24

Saturday
25

Sunday
26

Notes

I know what this one is !

It's one of those wines that by-passes your head and goes straight to your legs ...

Notes

June

Mon	Tue	Wed	Thu	Fri	Sat	Sun
					1	2
3	4	5	6	7	8	9
10	11	12	13	14	15	16
17	18	19	20	21	22	23
24	25	26	27	28	29	30

May/June

Monday
27

Holiday (UK)
Memorial Day (Holiday USA)

Tuesday
28

Wednesday
29

Thursday
30

Friday
31

Saturday
1

Sunday
2

Notes

June

Monday
3

Holiday (R. of Ireland)
King's Birthday (Holiday NZL)

Tuesday
4

Wednesday
5

Thursday
6   ●

Friday
7

Saturday
8

Sunday
9

Notes

June

Monday
10

Tuesday
11

Wednesday
12

Thursday
13

Friday
14

Saturday
15

Sunday
16

Father's Day (UK, R. of Ireland, USA, CAN)

Notes

June

Monday
17

Tuesday
18

Wednesday
19

Juneteenth (Holiday USA)

Thursday
20

Friday
21

○

Saturday
22

Sunday
23

Notes

June

Monday
24

Tuesday
25

Wednesday
26

Thursday
27

◐

Friday
28

Saturday
29

Sunday
30

Notes

Who else can I ring this time of night ...

... to spread some juicy gossip !

_____

_____

_____

_____

_____

_____

_____

_____

_____

_____

_____

_____

_____

_____

_____

_____

July

Mon	Tue	Wed	Thu	Fri	Sat	Sun
1	2	3	4	5	6	7
8	9	10	11	12	13	14
15	16	17	18	19	20	21
22	23	24	25	26	27	28
29	30	31				

July

Monday
1

Canada Day (Holiday CAN)

Tuesday
2

Wednesday
3

Thursday
4

Independence Day (Holiday USA)

	M	T	W	T	F	S	S	M	T	W	T	F	S	S	M
JUL	1	2	3	4	5	6	7	8	9	10	11	12	13	14	15

●

Friday
5

Saturday
6

Sunday
7

Notes

T W T F S S M T W T F S S M T W
16 17 18 19 20 21 22 23 24 25 26 27 28 29 30 31

July

Monday
8

Tuesday
9

Wednesday
10

Thursday
11

Friday
12

Battle of the Boyne (Holiday N. Ireland)

◐ Saturday
13

Sunday
14

Notes

July

Monday
15

Tuesday
16

Wednesday
17

Thursday
18

Friday
19

Saturday
20

○

Sunday
21

Notes

July

Monday
22

Tuesday
23

Wednesday
24

Thursday
25

Friday
26

Saturday
27

◑ Sunday
28

Notes

Enjoy the selective memory
that comes with age ! ...

Notes

August

Mon	Tue	Wed	Thu	Fri	Sat	Sun
			1	2	3	4
5	6	7	8	9	10	11
12	13	14	15	16	17	18
19	20	21	22	23	24	25
26	27	28	29	30	31	

Monday
29

Tuesday
30

Wednesday
31

Thursday
1

Notes

August

Monday
5

Holiday (SCT, R. of Ireland)

Tuesday
6

Wednesday
7

Thursday
8

Friday
9

Saturday
10

Sunday
11

Notes

August

Monday
12

Tuesday
13

Wednesday
14

Thursday
15

Friday
16

Saturday
17

Sunday
18

Notes

August

Monday
19   ○

Tuesday
20

Wednesday
21

Thursday
22

Friday
23

Saturday
24

Sunday
25

Notes

It's fabulous having grey hair !

... just ask any bald man ...

Notes

September

Mon	Tue	Wed	Thu	Fri	Sat	Sun
30						1
2	3	4	5	6	7	8
9	10	11	12	13	14	15
16	17	18	19	20	21	22
23	24	25	26	27	28	29

August/September

Holiday (UK except SCT)

	S	M	T	W	T	F	S	S	M	T	W	T	F	S	S
SEP	1	2	3	4	5	6	7	8	9	10	11	12	13	14	15

Friday
30

Saturday
31

Sunday
1

Father's Day (AUS, NZL)

Notes

September

Monday
2

Labor Day (Holiday USA)
Labour Day (Holiday CAN)

Tuesday
3   ●

Wednesday
4

Thursday
5

Friday
6

Saturday
7

Sunday
8

Notes

September

Monday
9

Tuesday
10

Wednesday
11

Thursday
12

Friday
13

Saturday
14

Sunday
15

Notes

September

Monday
16

Tuesday
17

Wednesday
18   ○

Thursday
19

Friday
20

Saturday
21

Sunday
22

Notes

September

Monday
23

Tuesday
24

◐

Wednesday
25

Thursday
26

Friday
27

Saturday
28

Sunday
29

Notes

To taste good, fish must swim 3 times ...

Once in water
Once in butter
Once in wine ...

Notes

_____

_____

_____

_____

_____

_____

_____

_____

_____

_____

_____

_____

_____

_____

_____

_____

_____

October

Mon	Tue	Wed	Thu	Fri	Sat	Sun
	1	2	3	4	5	6
7	8	9	10	11	12	13
14	15	16	17	18	19	20
21	22	23	24	25	26	27
28	29	30	31			

September/October

Monday
30

Tuesday
1

Wednesday
2

●

Thursday
3

Friday
4

Saturday
5

Sunday
6

Notes

W T F S S M T W T F S S M T W T
16 17 18 19 20 21 22 23 24 25 26 27 28 29 30 31

October

Monday
7

Tuesday
8

Wednesday
9

Thursday
10

Friday
11

Saturday
12

Sunday
13

Notes

October

Monday
14

Columbus Day (Holiday USA)
Thanksgiving Day (Holiday CAN)

Tuesday
15

Wednesday
16

Thursday
17

○

Notes

October

Monday
21

Tuesday
22

Wednesday
23

Thursday
24   ◑

Friday
25

Saturday
26

Sunday
27

British Summer Time ends

Notes

It's so time-consuming, not to mention humiliating, filling out these online thingies .

I have to go MILES down all the decades to get to my year of birth ...

Notes

November

Mon	Tue	Wed	Thu	Fri	Sat	Sun
				1	2	3
4	5	6	7	8	9	10
11	12	13	14	15	16	17
18	19	20	21	22	23	24
25	26	27	28	29	30	

October/November

Monday
28

Holiday (R. of Ireland)
Labour Day (Holiday NZL)

Tuesday
29

Wednesday
30

Thursday
31

Hallowe'en

	F	S	S	M	T	W	T	F	S	S	M	T	W	T	F
NOV	1	2	3	4	5	6	7	8	9	10	11	12	13	14	15

●

Diwali

Notes

S S M T W T F S S M T W T F S
16 17 18 19 20 21 22 23 24 25 26 27 28 29 30

November

Monday
4

Tuesday
5

Bonfire Night

Wednesday
6

Thursday
7

Friday
8

◐

Saturday
9

Sunday
10

Remembrance Sunday (UK)

Notes

November

Monday
11

Veterans Day (Holiday USA)
Remembrance Day (Holiday CAN)

Tuesday
12

Wednesday
13

Thursday
14

○

Friday
15

Saturday
16

Sunday
17

Notes

November

Monday
18

Tuesday
19

Wednesday
20

Thursday
21

Friday

22

◐

Saturday

23

Sunday

24

Notes

The male is a domestic animal which, if treated with firmness and kindness, can be trained to buy you dinner …

Notes

December

Mon	Tue	Wed	Thu	Fri	Sat	Sun
30	31					1
2	3	4	5	6	7	8
9	10	11	12	13	14	15
16	17	18	19	20	21	22
23	24	25	26	27	28	29

November/December

Monday
25

Tuesday
26

Wednesday
27

Thursday
28

Thanksgiving Day (Holiday USA)

	S	M	T	W	T	F	S	S	M	T	W	T	F	S	S
DEC	1	2	3	4	5	6	7	8	9	10	11	12	13	14	15

Friday
29

Saturday
30

St Andrew's Day

● Sunday
1

Notes

December

Monday
2

Holiday (SCT)

Tuesday
3

Wednesday
4

Thursday
5

Friday
6

Saturday
7

◑ Sunday
8

Notes

M T W T F S S M T W T F S S M T
16 17 18 19 20 21 22 23 24 25 26 27 28 29 30 31

December

Monday
9

Tuesday
10

Wednesday
11

Thursday
12

Friday
13

Saturday
14

○

Sunday
15

Notes

December

Monday
16

Tuesday
17

Wednesday
18

Thursday
19

Friday
20

Saturday
21

◑ Sunday
22

Notes

December

Monday
23

Tuesday
24

Christmas Eve

Wednesday
25

Christmas Day
(Holiday UK, R. of Ireland, USA, CAN, AUS, NZL)

Thursday
26

Boxing Day, St Stephen's Day
(Holiday UK, R. of Ireland, CAN, AUS, NZL)

	S	M	T	W	T	F	S	S	M	T	W	T	F	S	S
DEC	1	2	3	4	5	6	7	8	9	10	11	12	13	14	15

Friday

27

Saturday

28

Sunday

29

Notes

December/January '25

Monday
30

●

Tuesday
31

New Year's Eve

Wednesday
1

New Year's Day
(Holiday UK, R. of Ireland, USA, CAN, AUS, NZL)

Thursday
2

Holiday (SCT, NZL)

	W	T	F	S	S	M	T	W	T	F	S	S	M	T	W
JAN	1	2	3	4	5	6	7	8	9	10	11	12	13	14	15

Friday
3

Saturday
4

Sunday
5

Notes

Addresses

Addresses